A TRICKY kind of MAGIC

looking a bit more ominous out there mate -

Cheers Joodz for all the chats + malarky - here's to many more -

NIGEL BAINES

HODDER

HODDER CHILDREN'S BOOKS

FIRST PUBLISHED IN GREAT BRITAIN IN 2023 BY HODDER & STOUGHTON

1 3 5 7 9 10 8 6 4 2

TEXT AND ILLUSTRATIONS COPYRIGHT © NIGEL BAINES, 2023

THE MORAL RIGHT OF THE AUTHOR HAS BEEN ASSERTED.

A CIP CATALOGUE RECORD FOR THIS BOOK IS AVAILABLE FROM THE BRITISH LIBRARY.

ISBN 978 1 444 96026 6

PRINTED AND BOUND IN GREAT BRITAIN BY
CLAYS LTD. ELCOGRAF S.P.A.

THE PAPER AND BOARD USED IN THIS BOOK
ARE MADE FROM WOOD FROM RESPONSIBLE SOURCES.

MIX
Paper from
responsible sources
FSC® C104740

HODDER CHILDREN'S BOOKS
AN IMPRINT OF
HACHETTE CHILDREN'S GROUP
PART OF HODDER & STOUGHTON
CARMELITE HOUSE
50 VICTORIA EMBANKMENT
LONDON EC4Y 0DZ

AN HACHETTE UK COMPANY
WWW.HACHETTE.CO.UK

WWW.HACHETTECHILDRENS.CO.UK

Everyone needs a Rori
and a Rabbit in life.
I've been so lucky.
You know who you are.
N.B.

2

3

Show me, Cooper, do it again.

You get some invisible tape and tape the toothpick to your thumb like this.

The audience can't see the tape ...

6

This is me. Cooper Stanley. 'Good at tricks and jokes but lives in another world.' That's what my school report said. Fin, he's my little brother.

Fin takes up a lot of Mum's time. Imagine watching a television that changes channels every ten seconds. That's Fin. A one-kid earthquake.

FIN!

And then there was Dad. Dad was great ...

... the greatest.

Dad was an electrician but in his spare time
he was a magician called the Great Eduardo
(his real name was Eddie).

His shows were more electric than his work.
He taught me so many things, like how
to do some of the old classic tricks.

I remember Dad doing a fantastic trick where he made a ball float in mid air! He told me the ball was able to float as it was from a mystical tribe of people and was filled with special magic.

I really believed it!! That's what good magicians do, make you believe things that make no sense. Dad showed me how it worked, the ball had a little hole in the back he stuck his thumb in, but I still thought it was magic.

Years ago magicians used a special rabbit prop called a kicker. It's a toy rabbit with a spring inside. A skilled magician can hold it and make it move and look like a real live rabbit.

Dad found one in an antique shop and used it in his shows. He would pretend he was being attacked by the rabbit and he'd wrestle it to the floor.

Other times he would stroke it and make it look real. The audience would all go 'aaaah' and then Dad would boot it across the stage. The audience would be shocked until Dad explained!

Anyway, the rabbit he used is still in my room. Dad thought it looked really tough as it had become so battered. So he called it Rabbit De Niro after his favourite film star.

So you might have noticed that when I talk about my dad I always say 'was' and not 'is'. That's because a few weeks ago Dad died suddenly. Yup, that was pretty grim and I still don't understand it. The Great Eduardo did the worst vanishing trick of all.

Just like that.

CHAPTER THREE

THE NEXT DAY

So I said, 'Can I have an ice cream?'

And he said 'hundreds and thousands?' 'No thanks,' I said, 'just the one'.

HA HA!

HA!!

GROAN!

Now this next trick is so risky I could break my neck doing it so ...

MAGIC BLANKET

I'll need your applause now in advance in case it goes wrong!

He's floating!

Cool!!

WHOOO! COOOOPER!!

Thank you!

Ha Ha! His shoes are stuck together!

23

10 MINUTES LATER

GASP

WHEEZE

I shouldn't have got angry with Tori. Why do we always get angry with the people we like the most?

Ever since Dad died people have been weird around me. Adults are the worst, saying things like:

I'm sorry you lost your dad.

WHAT I WISH I HAD SAID

I didn't lose him! He died. Why would I lose him? I lost the school hamster, I lost my phone once, I lost my favourite sock but I didn't lose my dad. He's gone and it's not my fault!!

WHAT I REALLY SAID

Uhm. Yeah. Thanks.

It's the same at school. After Dad died it was like the other kids suddenly started to avoid me. Like my head was a huge sad-faced emoji and they might catch something!

So I make people laugh. Even when I want to do the exact opposite of laughing. I like making people laugh and doing Dad's tricks but it feels wrong to laugh when I should be sad.

Or is it? I don't know. I feel like my brain was taken out by grief aliens who have replaced it with a TV remote ... zapper?

ZAP

I remember one Christmas when Dad did a show and he dressed half as a woman and half as a sailor. He would turn one way and then the other to make it look like he was having a conversation between two people. I laughed so hard that banana milkshake came out of my nose. Now I feel like two in one. Half of me is Cooper who is funny and does tricks and half is Cooper who feels like he is on an out-of-control rollercoaster. Also, it's not so funny this time.

CHAPTER FOUR

Is that you, Coops love?

Yeah.

Can you get Fin some juice from the fridge?

There should be some beetroot, watermelon, spinach and ginger juice in there. Don't drink it all love, leave some for your mum!

Mum comes up with the weirdest juice combinations. If it fits in a blender we will probably have had it for breakfast. Come to think of it, I haven't seen Fin's sock puppet Dad made for him. I've an awful feeling we had it for dinner last week.

Eurgh!

Here you go, Fin, a nice glass of dead vegetable juice.

Oh and Cooper, could you just pop out to the shop and get some more lentils and a packet of wild rice and some ...

You know when adults ask you to just 'pop out' it means they want you to do something that is going to take them too long to do themselves.

34

CHAPTER FIVE

CHAPTER SIX

THE NEXT MORNING

I'm sure Mum is making me drink juice made from cardboard and Fin's old nappies.

Mum, can't we just have orange juice from a carton? Dad used to let us.

But it was packed with sugar, Coops. The last thing you boys need is more sugar. If it was up to your dad he would have let you eat doughnuts and gummy bears for breakfast.

But Dad ...

... is not here, Coops, and I need help in the house and with Fin.

I know.

So can you just help me with the washing up?

Do me a trick, Cooper!

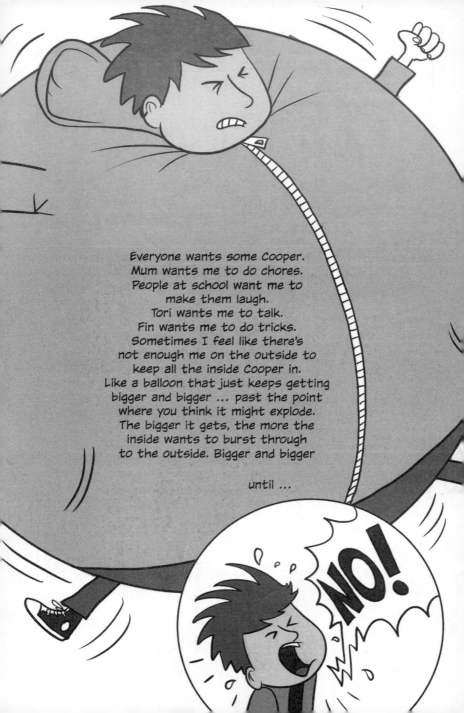

At least, it was supposed to slam for dramatic effect but we have these new thick carpets

and sometimes the door gets stuck in the new carpet so instead of a big dramatic slam you get a funny 'pswiiish' which isn't dramatic at all.

Rough day, eh, kiddo?

You know, the next time you decide to send me on a flying mission, just go easy on my butt – it's a highly specialised piece of equipment.

Who's there?

I mean, I should complain to the League for the Protection of Magic Rabbits. We're just not built for aerodynamic adventures.

Rabbit?

Whoa! Go easy on the grip there!!

CHAPTER SEVEN

Hare-o-plane, aeroplane ... hare ... like a rabbit ...

Come on, let's get some breakfast.

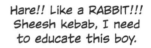

Hare!! Like a RABBIT!!! Sheesh kebab, I need to educate this boy.

SNIFF

I know, s'OK.

It's weird when you most want to tell someone how you feel it's like words get all panicky in your head and on the way down just forget to come out of your mouth and head straight into your stomach.

Mum seems OK but it is hard to tell. She has her meditation face on more often these days. Dad used to say she was probably the tallest person on earth as her head was often way up in the clouds.

I need some air after that rabbit scare so after breakfast I head to the mall.

Hey, Magic Man's here! Do us a trick, Coops mate.

Hey, it's a good job zombies eat brains as he'll be safe!

What the ... ?

No, No, NO!!

How did you get in MY BAG?!

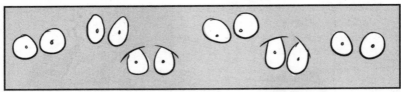

CHAPTER EIGHT

THE NEXT MORNING

YAWN

Oh great, a spot.

As big as an asteroid too.

Gross.

Maybe there's some spot cream here.

Cooper, this isn't happening to you. You need to slap yourself round the face with a cold watermelon. This is a toy. A toy you put into the rubbish.

Woah there, less of the 'toy', that's racist.

How can it be raci— I mean, why am I even talking to you?!

Well, it's rabbitist then ...

... as is leaving me in the trash, that was a rough night.

I'm not listening la la la la la la la la la

Oh you know, the usual stuff. Two million Instagram followers, school vanishing into a wormhole, making millions from going on tour with an old toy rabbit that talks.

Less of the old!

You know that's not what you REALLY want.

We both miss him.

So what if I told you we could still find him?

Magic isn't just fast hands and hidden doors, there's real magic.

Life ain't the same, buddy, and we can get him back and make things like they used to be.

But ... how? I mean, this feels like a dream.

Just imagine it, kid. The rabbit gets to pull the magician out of the hat. How cool will that be?

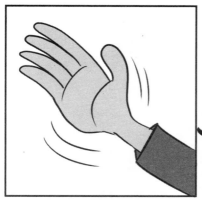

CHAPTER NINE

It really is amazing how you do that, Cooper.

Tori?

I'm sorry I freaked out the other day.

That's OK.

Well, it's not really. I've been, so ... um ... well, I think I've found something. Something really weird and big and important.

Oh?

Well, you know magic is all about tricking the eye and the brain. I saw this YouTube magician give a talk once. He said there's a gap between what you think you see and what is actually there.

MUM HAS BEEN IN HER OWN WORLD ALL THE TIME LATELY

AND I WAS IN MY UPSIDE DOWN ONE AND SO ... AND SO ... I THREW A TERRIBLE STINK BOMB INTO THE ROOM *

*(not a real one, that would have been better)

HERE IT COMES

MUM!! Please stop. How can you do your yoga and pull those peaceful faces all the time? It's like you don't miss Dad at all.

WHAM!

Well, crazy or not, I need to do something.

OK buddy, let's find him.

SLAM!

Dad once told me that roads were not always around.
People built them in the paths that were used most.
He said people still did this. If you look at parks or
grassy corners on the street, you'll see a path
that has been trodden down to make a short cut.
These were called 'desire paths'. Paths made by
people's desire to go somewhere on their own.
So, when you don't know where you're going,
anywhere is the right direction.
Just make your own path.

CHAPTER TEN

It was raining. Not just any rain. This was as though it were being dropped on purpose.

When Mum comes back from the supermarket loaded with bags she drops them in a heap as soon as she comes in the door. It was just like that, like the clouds had got so tired of carrying all that rain that they just dropped it in one soggy lump and went for a cup of tea.

Especially the banana zingblaster ones.

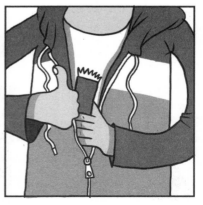

86

CHAPTER ELEVEN

Quick, in here!

Here, we can hide behind this curtain.

SEVERAL HUNDRED SECONDS LATER

Why hasn't he come through the door yet?

CLosed

keep OUT

Abandoned

Wow, look at this stuff!

Dad had a vanishing cabinet just like this ... it's identical!!

See, I told you, kid.

We're on the trail.

What a place. How come I've never seen it before?!

Hey, it's a palanquin*!!!*

What in the name of the Easter Bunny is a pandabling?

Well, they used them to carry emperors around in. Magicians also used them.

There's a false bottom inside. The assistant would climb in, lift the trapdoor and hide. When the magician opened the curtains it looked like the assistant had vanished.

Hee Hee!

CHAPTER TWELVE

Maybe he's right.

Look! Carrot ends. There's rabbit folk around here!

You're right. You know, I've never understood what it is with rabbits and carrots.

Oh it goes way back into ancient Bunny Lore. I mean, they're good for your eyes — when did you last see a rabbit with glasses?

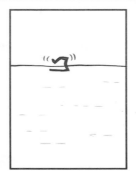

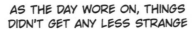

AS THE DAY WORE ON, THINGS DIDN'T GET ANY LESS STRANGE

WE SAW MORE AND MORE RABBITS

CHAINED SACKS BOUNCING ALONG

AND SEVERAL MORE OF THOSE IRRITATING PLAYING CARDS

Pick a card. Any card, go on!

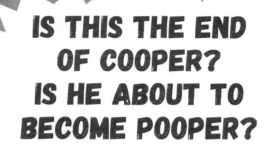

IS THIS THE END OF COOPER? IS HE ABOUT TO BECOME POOPER?

You know we could have filled the rest of the book with blank pages. (Yeah, I know, it's unlikely but we're trying to build some tension here.)

ALL SEEMS LOST. HONEST. BUT ... WAIT A MINUTE ...

Sorry, old friend.

Thanks. For a machine it had really sweaty hands.

Let's head for that hill and out of this house and gloopy mess.

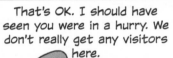

So, did anyone else come along before me?

I'm not sure. I spend most of my time sorting out wrong magic.

You see, I'm looking for my dad. Where I'm from is ... well ... Dad ... well, he sort of vanished and Rabbit thought we could find him and then, well ... we thought it might be magic.

It probably sounds stupid.

No, not stupid. But magic is tricky. We want to believe something ...

... and our eyes are not always quick enough to see the truth.

My dad used to say that we believe in our eyes too much.

He told me once that if you look in a mirror and try to see your own eyes move, you can't, even though our eyes move constantly.

It is because the brain doesn't show us everything the eye sees, it makes it easier for us to have a stable view of the world.

Otherwise it would be like watching a film shot with a wobbly camera. Our brain edits what we see.

So for those tiny milliseconds we are blind, and if you added up all those tiny blind bits we would be blind for four hours a day!

And that's where magicians work. In our blind spots.

He sounds like a clever man.

He was. I mean is ... I mean, I don't even know. That's why we're here, to find him. I'm sure he is here.

But I just don't even know where here is.

Hmmm ... well. So, did you ever do a trick that didn't work, Cooper? Something that didn't vanish when it should have or didn't reappear, or a card that was the wrong one?

CHAPTER FIFTEEN

... these rabbits never got to be pulled out of a magician's hat. They're stuck here.

You've actually been pulled out of a hat. You're probably like a god to them.

Well, my dad was pulled from a hat and so was his dad before him. I come from a long line of hat-pulled rabbits.

It's nothing special, I guess.

MANY ACHING HOURS LATER

Cooper, can we rest for a bit?

No problem. Actually, he's heavier than you think.

I think you'll find it is mostly muscle.

SHUFFLE

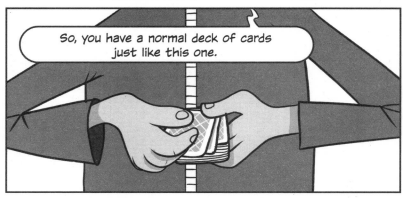

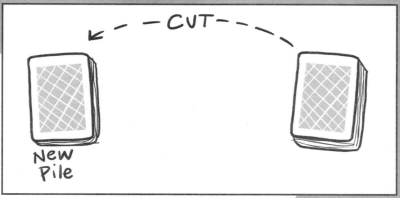

Now take the top card from the middle pile and place it face down on the left hand pile.

And now take the next card from the middle pile and place that face down on the right hand pile.

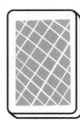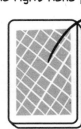

Now, Rori, pick up the next card in the middle pile. This is the magic one! Don't show me, look at it and remember it. Then put it back face down anywhere you like on any of the three piles.

Now put the three piles back any way you like and give them a good shuffle and mix up. Then when you've done that I take the cards and press them to my head ...

... and I utter the magic incantation. This is very important.

ITCHY BUMS AND PINK MEERKATS AND A BUCKETFUL OF EARWAX.

Your card is the Three of Diamonds!

IT IS!!!

Stars are so far away that some of the ones we see don't actually exist. They are so far from us that by the time the light from them reaches us they have died. They're not there any more but we can still see them.

So I guess there is always magic in the universe.

Cooper ... what's a Ferrari?

CHAPTER SEVENTEEN

Come on, I'll race you.

THERE WAS A HERD OF ESCAPOLOGISTS

A DECK OF UNPICKED CARDS

MARCHING WANDS AND FUNNY MAGIC ROPE

AND THEN

It's the palanquin!

It's Dimblechip!

But how did he get hold of the palanquin?

I'm more interested in how he manages to fit his head inside it.

They seem to be happy bunnies though.

HALT!

CREAK

CHAPTER EIGHTEEN

So you say you came from your world to here in the palanquin?

I knew there was a door to magic somewhere.

If what you say is true then you must have arrived when I was over the other side of Magic World tending my crop of silk hankies. I parked the palanquin there. I always travel in it.

Hmmm ... it's a long way, you have had quite a journey.

The weather out there is much better for my silk hankies, you know.

SNIGGER

IT'S NOT FUNNY!!!

No matter. Hmmm ... I see you've met one of our big-eared friends.

Well, let's get him a little friend.

Et voila ... what the ...?

NOT FUNNY NOT FUNNY!!

CHUCKLE

STOMP

STAMP

SO, RABBIT AND I EXPLAINED THE WHOLE STORY SO FAR

... Dad

... the magic

... Dad not being there

... the dreams

... home

... feeling lost

... Rabbit

... the argument

... running away

Indeed I did. He is a searcher like yourself. Only he was seeking out more advanced magic, the perfect way to do tricks.

Dad ... DAD!!! Where can I find him, please ... ?

For that, Cooper, I need you to perform a magic show for me.

Cooper performed like he had three pairs of arms. He magicked like he had never magicked before.

You left his card in the palanquin and you left me with an idea.

THE GREAT EDUARDO
☆ MAGICIAN ☆

You will stay here and teach me magic. This will no longer be a land where magic doesn't work and when it does I can conquer this world and yours!

The palanquin will be destroyed too so there will be NO GOING BACK for you!

NOW LOCK THEM UP!!!

CHAPTER TWENTY-ONE

It's all over, Rori. Dad isn't coming back, is he? There's no magic after all.

I'm so sorry you lost your dad. But you've not lost his love, or your mum's. You never will. It stays with you.

And don't forget your brother Fin.

You're not just a big brother. You're a link ...

... a vital one between the dad you knew and the one Fin needs to know about.

In a funny way I think you've found your dad, Cooper. You found your love for him.

Rabbit, you've always been there for me and nothing reminds me more of Dad than you do.

I'm not crying. I think I've just got carrot dust in my eye.

And thank you, Rori. You are so right. You know, it's Fin's birthday soon ...

... and I'm going to be there.

We need to stop Dimblechip destroying the palanquin so you can get back. But first ... how do we get out of here?

CHAPTER TWENTY-TWO

So how do we get past the rabbit guards?

Those are wild Bolivian Guard Rabbits. Surprisingly strong with big, sharp, pointy teeth.

What about, what do you call it? Your rug sack. Is there anything in there that could help?

OF COURSE! That's it!!!

When I was little I remember being in the car at night on quiet country roads. Rabbits would suddenly run into the road and get hypnotised by the lights. They would just stand there like were in a trance.

210

Now look into the lights, my friend.

Is it working?

We need something else. Make a noise like a car.

CHAPTER TWENTY-THREE

Come on, we need to find that palanquin.

If that's the case then the vessel doesn't matter. We just need a new one.

It's obvious.

MAGIC HATS!!

Come on. We passed a field of them when we were on the way to Dimblechip Towers.

CHAPTER TWENTY-FOUR

If I remember the field is just over ...

... here.

228

CHAPTER TWENTY-FIVE

Look, Fizzy Rainbow Sticks. That must be the way back.

Ooh, I feel faint!

What will you do now, Rori?

This is my world and it will be put right now.

These rabbits will need some looking after and there's a lot of wrong magic they can help me put right.

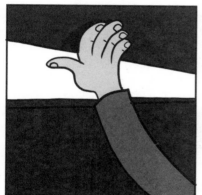

CHAPTER TWENTY-SIX

I am sorry, Mum.

I miss Dad and ... well, I sometimes don't know who I am any more or what to do.

I know, Coops. We will always miss him.

When my dad died I felt lost. I still miss him.

But it doesn't hurt in the same way. You fall, you cut your knee. The pain is not nice but it doesn't last for ever but you will aways have a little scar to remind you. Look at Rabbit here. He's got that patch on his eye. It was a sad day when it happened. It's not sad now though. It's part of his story.

Ta Da!

I thought Rabbit was looking a bit tired so I bought him a friend.

243

I just wanted to run and keep running. I felt like a coward.

Cooper ... a coward! You must be the bravest person I know.

Admitting you're scared and feel lost. Only the bravest people do that.

Everyone gets stuck in stinky goo at some point!

But ... how?

As your dad would say, there's stage magic and real magic. But real magic happens inside us and doesn't look so amazing as big stage fireworks! He'd be so proud of you.

245

NIGEL BAINES

Even though his name is an anagram of Alien Beings, according to the label on his side he is 100% human. He is a full-time writer, illustrator, thinker, designer, and should win some sort of national award for tea consumption. He has illustrated over eighty children's books, including *Spud Goes Green* which won the Blue Peter Best Book of Facts and *The Covers of My Book Are Too Far Apart* which was nominated for the Kate Greenaway award.

Putting words and pictures together is the best and makes up for never having scored a goal at Wembley or opened the batting for England. He once did stand-up comedy to a room that responded with monastic silence, has been canoed to a jungle hospital and once knocked himself out celebrating his team scoring a goal. He lives in Hertfordshire with his sofa and an enormous pile of teabags.

The best advice he can give to anyone is don't just do something. Sit there. You never know what you might think of.

His name is also an anagram of Been Sailing which are the two words he would like to be remembered by.